DEVELOPING SCIENCE LANGUAGE

for

Physical Processes

with

8−9

year olds

Charlotte Clarke

Published by Scholastic Ltd,
Villiers House,
Clarendon Avenue,
Leamington Spa,
Warwickshire CV32 5PR
Visit our website at www.scholastic.co.uk

Printed by Alden Group Ltd, Oxford

© 2001 Scholastic Ltd
Text © Charlotte Clarke 2001

1 2 3 4 5 6 7 8 9 0 1 2 3 4 5 6 7 8 9 0

AUTHOR
Charlotte Clarke

LITERACY CONSULTANT
Gill Matthews

EDITOR
Joel Lane

ASSISTANT EDITOR
David Sandford

SERIES DESIGNER
Rachael Hammond

DESIGNER
Erik Ivens

COVER PHOTOGRAPH
© Martyn Chillmaid

ILLUSTRATIONS
Theresa Tibbetts

British Library Cataloguing-in-Publication Data
A catalogue record for this book is available from the British Library.

ISBN 0-439-01874-9

Designed using Adobe Pagemaker

The right of Charlotte Clarke to be identified as the Author of this
work has been asserted by her in accordance with the Copyright,
Designs and Patents Act 1988.

CONTENTS

CONTENTS

INTRODUCTION

Children often struggle to remember science words. Sometimes the words seem strange or unusual, and sometimes the words we use in science have other meanings. Think about these science words: *force, material, property, sink.* If you ask a child what these words mean, you are likely to get responses such as: 'If you force someone to do something, it's not very nice'; 'My coat is made of material'; 'My things are my property'; 'The sink is where we wash up after painting'. But when children go into science lessons, we sometimes assume that they already understand a 'force' to be a push or a pull, a 'material' to be any substance, a 'property' to be how a material behaves, and 'sink' to be what some things do in water.

Scientific language

This series aims to give children practice in using science words, both through science activities and in real-life contexts, so that they become familiar with the scientific meanings of these words. Use of correct scientific vocabulary is essential for high attainment in SATs. The QCA *Scheme of Work for Science* (DfEE) for Key Stages 1 and 2 in England suggests examples of vocabulary for each of its units; although these books are not divided into exactly the same topics, the QCA vocabulary and its progressive introduction are used as the basis for the word selection here.

The science covered is divided into units based on topics from the national curricula for England, Northern Ireland, Wales and Scotland. In this book, the science is drawn from the 'Physical processes' statements for ages 8–9 relating to electricity, forces, light, sound, the Earth and space, and energy. The series of boxed letters at the bottom of each page shows in which curriculum documents the focus of each activity occurs. For example, for the activity on page 15, the boxes E NI W S indicate that the activity focuses on a topic from all the curricula except Northern Ireland.

Science and literacy

The National Literacy Strategy for England suggests teaching objectives and gives examples of the types of activity that children should encounter during each year of primary school. This book uses many of these techniques for developing children's understanding and use of scientific language. The activities are mainly intended for use in science time, as they have been written with science learning objectives in mind. However, some of the activities could be used in literacy time. Science texts have already been published for use in literacy time, but many of them use science content appropriate for older children.

During literacy time you need to be focusing on language skills, not teaching new science. It is with this in mind that these sheets, drawing from age-appropriate science work, have been produced. It is also suggested that these sheets are used in literacy time, only after the science content has been introduced in science time.

The series focuses on paper-based activities to develop scientific language, but it is hoped that you might use some of the ideas in planning practical science activities.

About this book

Each unit in this book begins with a non-fiction text that introduces some key scientific vocabulary. The key words are highlighted in bold type. The texts cover a range of non-fiction genres.

Following this text are two comprehension activities that help children to identify and understand the key words (and a range of additional science words). They are pitched at two levels:

 for older or more able children

 for younger or less able children.

Although the comprehension activities are designed to be used mainly during science time, you may wish to use the texts as examples of non-fiction writing in the Literacy Hour. The comprehension pages contain two or three types of question (a change of icon indicates a change in the type of question):

 The answer can be found in the text.

 Children will need to think about the answer. These questions usually elicit science understanding beyond what the text provides.

 An activity aimed at developing children's literacy skills. These are optional extension activities for individual or group work, with teacher support if necessary.

Following the comprehension pages in each unit are activities aimed at developing children's understanding and use of the key vocabulary. These include: completing charts, describing, matching pictures and writing, labelling, sequencing, analysing graphs and tables, making books, matching sentence starters to endings, cloze text, text marking, writing instructions, identifying true and false statements, 'round the class' card games, making dictionaries.

WORD LIST

Electricity words

bare wire
battery
break
bulb
bulb holder
buzzer
circuit
circuit diagram
closed switch
complete circuit
component
conductor
connection
crocodile clip
electric shock
electrician
electricity
graphite
insulator
metal
motor
plastic
plug
safety
socket
switch
symbol
wire

Forces words

aluminium
attract
direction
force
friction
iron
like poles
magnet
magnetic

magnetic force
non-magnetic
opposite
pole
pull
push
repel
rough
smooth
steel
stretch
surface
unlike poles

Sound words

air
ears
gas
hear
high
liquid
listen
loud
low
musical instrument
quiet
silence
soft
solid
sound
travel
tuning fork
vibrate
vibration
voice box

Light words

block
bright
clear

dark
day
dim
direction
distance
higher
length
light
light source
longer
material
midday
night
object
opaque
position
shadow
shorter
Sun
torch
translucent
transparent

Space words

axis
dark
darkness
day
daytime
Earth
east
evening
horizon
light
lit
month
Moon
night
revolve
rise
rotate

set
space
sphere
spherical
Sun
sunlight
sunrise
sunset
sky
west

Energy words

cables
coal
dam
electrical energy
electricity
energy
fuel
furnace
gas
generator
heat
light
movement
non-renewable
oil
power station
pylon
renewable
sound
source
turbine
water power
wind power

Circuit components

To make an **electric circuit**, you need these things.

First of all, a **battery**. This supplies the **electricity**. Then you need other **components** such as **bulbs**, **buzzers**, **motors**, **switches** and **wires**.

A **bulb** will light up when it is **connected** in a **circuit**, a **buzzer** will make a sound, and a **motor** will make things spin round. You can use a motor to make a piece of card spin round.

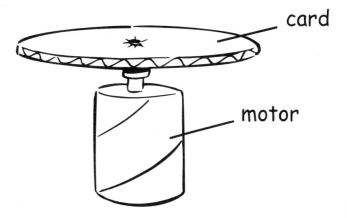

card

motor

You need a **switch** to turn other components on and off. If you don't use a switch, the battery will quickly run down. The **wires connect** together all the components in the circuit. They often have **crocodile clips** on the ends to make this easier.

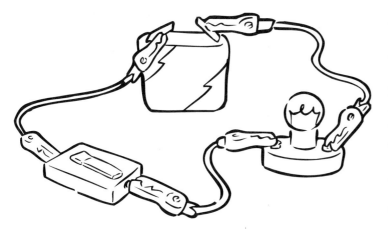

When you are connecting things up in a circuit, you need to make sure you have a **complete circuit** where all the components are joined up in a loop, and there are no gaps.

If there is a gap in the circuit, we call it a **break**. A break in the circuit shown in the picture above would mean that the bulb would not light.

Circuit components

1. What is the first thing you need to make an electric circuit?

_____

2. What is the job of the battery? _____

_____

3. What are the jobs of these things?

bulb _____

buzzer _____

motor _____

switch _____

wires _____

4. What happens to the battery if you don't have a switch in the

circuit? _____

5. Draw a complete circuit.   6. Draw a circuit with a break in it.

Write a list of instructions for making a complete circuit.

Circuit components

1. To make a circuit, first of all you need a _____.

Complete these sentences about what components do.

2. A battery _____ the _____.

3. A bulb _____ _____.

4. A buzzer makes ___ _____.

5. A motor makes things _____ _____.

6. A switch _____.

7. The wires _____ everything together.

8. If you don't use a switch, what will happen to the battery?

_____

Tick the correct box.
9. In a complete circuit, there are **gaps** ◯ **no gaps** ◯ .

10. In a complete circuit, the switch is **open** ◯ **closed** ◯ .

11. Tick the drawing that shows a complete circuit.

◯   ◯   ◯

12. If there is a break in the circuit in the pictures

above, the bulb will _____ _____.

Write a list of instructions for making a circuit.

Electrical components

Label the components in each of these circuits. Use the words in the box to help you.

| wire   crocodile clip   battery   buzzer   motor   bulb   switch |

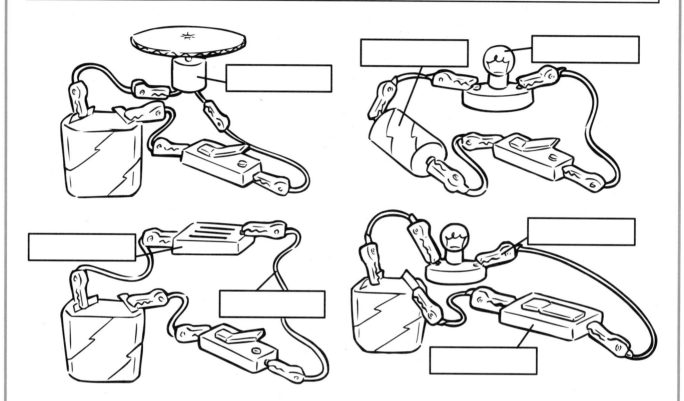

In two of these circuits, the bulb will not light. Say which circuits they are and explain why.

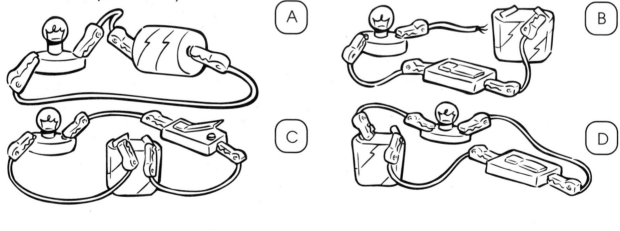

_____

_____

_____

_____

Which component?

Which component would you need to put into a circuit to make each of these things? Write the names of the components beside the pictures. The words you need are in the box.

bulb	buzzer	motor	bulb	buzzer	motor	bulb

toy roundabout

doorbell

torch

doll's house

fan

steady-hand game

cat with light-up eyes

What components do you need to make **all** of these things work?

Different types of switches

These switches all do different jobs.

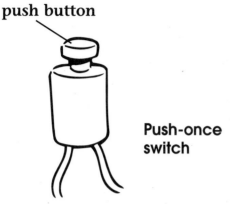

push button

Push-once switch

When you let go, the button comes **up** again to **break** the **circuit**.

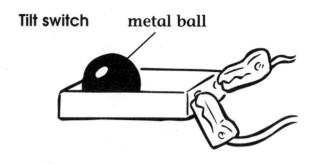

Tilt switch   metal ball

When the switch is **tipped** up, the metal ball **connects** the two wires and **completes** the circuit.

Two-way switch

The switch can be moved to connect with the **metal** part at A **or** B.

push button

Push-twice switch

The button stays **down** after you push it, until you push it a second time to **break** the circuit.

Say which switch you would use for each of these jobs, and explain why.

To make a light come on when a lorry is tipped up. _____

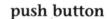

_____

To ring a doorbell. _____

JONES

_____

To turn a light on, so it stays on. _____

_____

To make a blue light and a red light flash in turn. _____

_____

_____

Circuits crossword

Write your own clues for this crossword.

¹b	u	l	b	■	²b	u	z	z	e	r	■	■	■	■
■	■	■	■	■	a	■	■	■	■	³c	■	■	■	
■	■	■	⁴m	o	t	o	r	■	■	r	■	■	■	
■	⁵c	■	■	■	t	■	■	■	■	o	■	⁶w	■	
⁷c	o	m	p	l	e	t	e	c	i	r	c	u	i	t
■	n	■	■	■	r	■	■	■	■	o	■	r	■	
■	n	■	■	■	y	■	■	■	■	d	■	e	■	
■	e	■	■	■	■	■	■	■	■	i	■	s	■	
■	⁸c	o	m	p	o	n	e	n	t	■	l	■	■	■
■	t	■	■	■	■	■	■	■	■	e	■	■	■	
■	i	■	■	■	■	⁹s	w	i	t	c	h	■	■	
■	o	■	■	■	■	■	■	■	■	l	■	■	■	
■	n	■	¹⁰c	l	o	s	e	d	s	w	i	t	c	h
■	■	■	■	■	■	■	■	■	■	p	■	■	■	

Across

1. This lights up when it is connected to a battery.

2. _____

    _____

4. _____

    _____

7. _____

    _____

8. _____

    _____

9. _____

    _____

10. _____

    _____

Down

2. This supplies the electricity to make the circuit work.

3. _____

    _____

5. _____

    _____

6. _____

    _____

Circuits card game

Teacher instructions

Photocopy onto card. Cut along the dotted lines. Fold each card in half along the solid line, with the text on the outside, and fasten with adhesive tape.

If you are working with a small group, give each child a card. If you are working with the whole class, share the cards out one between two or three. All the cards must be given out.

The child (or group) with the card marked * reads the question aloud. The child (or group) with the answer to that question reads it out, then reads out the question on the back of that card. This goes on until the first child (or group) has read out the answer on the first card.

fold

Q	* What do we call it when electrical components are connected in a circle?	A	components
Q	This supplies electricity.	A	a circuit
Q	This lights up.	A	a battery
Q	This makes a sound.	A	a bulb
Q	This spins around.	A	a buzzer
Q	This makes other components go on and off.	A	a motor
Q	These connect all the components in a circuit.	A	a switch
Q	A complete circuit has…	A	wires
Q	In a complete circuit, the switch must be…	A	no gaps
Q	If there is a gap in a circuit, we call this a…	A	closed
Q	If there is a break in a circuit, will the components work?	A	break
Q	If you leave a bulb in a circuit on too long, what will happen to the battery?	A	no
Q	What is the general name for batteries, bulbs, wires, buzzers, motors and switches?	A	it will run down

Drawing circuits

Diane is an **electrician**. She works for many people, fixing electrical problems. She has to know about being **safe** with **electricity**. She has to know about **circuits** and how they work. Sometimes she has to follow instructions when working on a circuit.

The instructions need to be easy to understand. Instead of drawing pictures, electricians use special **symbols** for the **components** they use. All electricians use the same symbols so that they can understand each other's instructions. Here are some of the symbols they use:

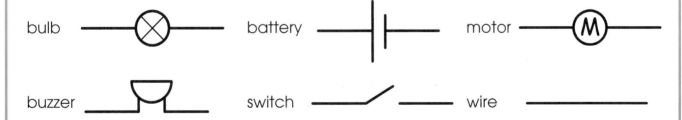

Instead of drawing pictures of circuits, they draw **circuit diagrams**.

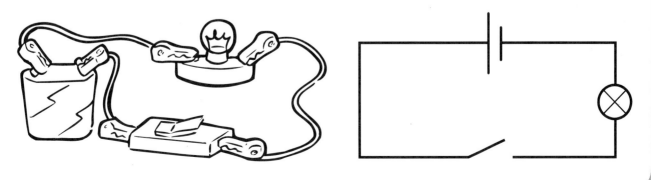

Drawing circuits

1. What is Diane's job? _____

2. Diane has to know how _____ work.

3. What do electricians use instead of drawing pictures of the components in a circuit? _____

_____

4. Why do they all use the same symbols? _____

_____

5. What are their drawings of circuits called?

_____

6. Label the components in these circuits.

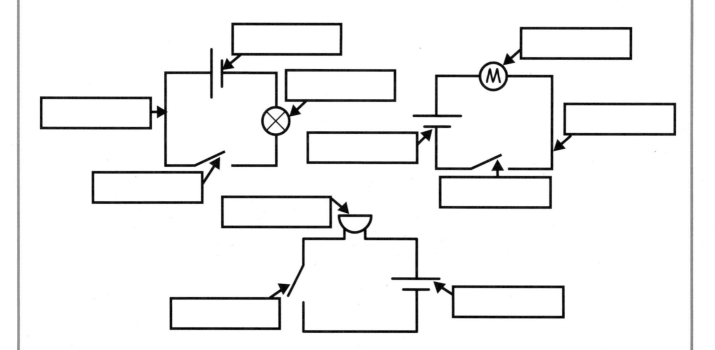

7. On another sheet of paper, draw a circuit with a battery, wires, two bulbs and a switch. Use a ruler to draw straight lines.

Imagine you are an electrician and you need someone else to work with you. Write down what sort of person you would want. What skills would he or she need?

Drawing circuits

Fill in the blanks or circle the correct answer.

1.   What is Diane's job? _____

2.   Diane has to know about **circuits / pipes / bricks**.

3.   Instead of drawing a picture of each component (such as a bulb),

electricians use special _____

4.   Draw the correct symbols in the boxes.

bulb   [   ]   wire   [   ]

battery [   ]   switch   [   ]

5.   What is an electrician's drawing of a circuit called?

_____

6.   Label the parts of the circuit in this circuit diagram by copying the words on the right.

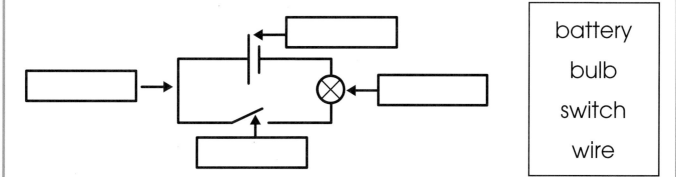

battery
bulb
switch
wire

7.   On another sheet of paper, draw a circuit with a battery, wires, a motor and a switch. Use a ruler to draw straight lines.

Imagine you are an electrician and you need someone else to work with you. Write down what sort of person you would want. What skills would he or she need? Ask your teacher for some sentence starters to help you.

Match the pictures

Cut out these circuit pictures and circuit diagrams. Match the pictures to the correct diagrams. One picture does not have a circuit diagram to go with it. Draw the circuit diagram for it in the blank box.

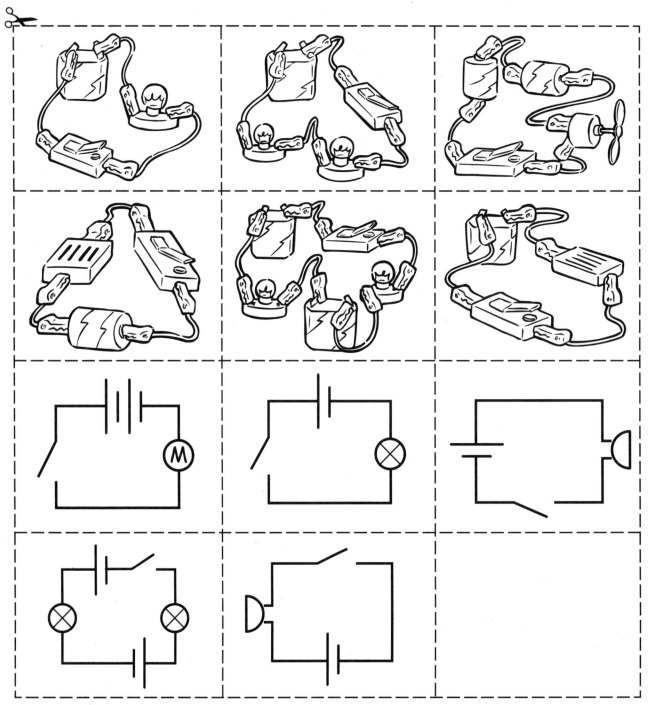

Label one component in each circuit diagram, using each of these words:

battery	bulb	motor	wire	buzzer	switch

Circuit drawing game

Teacher instructions
Cut out the cards. Sit the children in pairs, back to back. Give a card to one child in each pair.
The other child should not see the card. The child with the card should try to describe the
diagram to his or her partner, who should try to draw it. The child describing the diagram
must not say what each symbol looks like, but should use the names of the components and
describe their positions in the circuit. Encourage the children to compare their completed
diagrams to the ones on the cards. More able children could try the harder examples at the
bottom of the sheet.

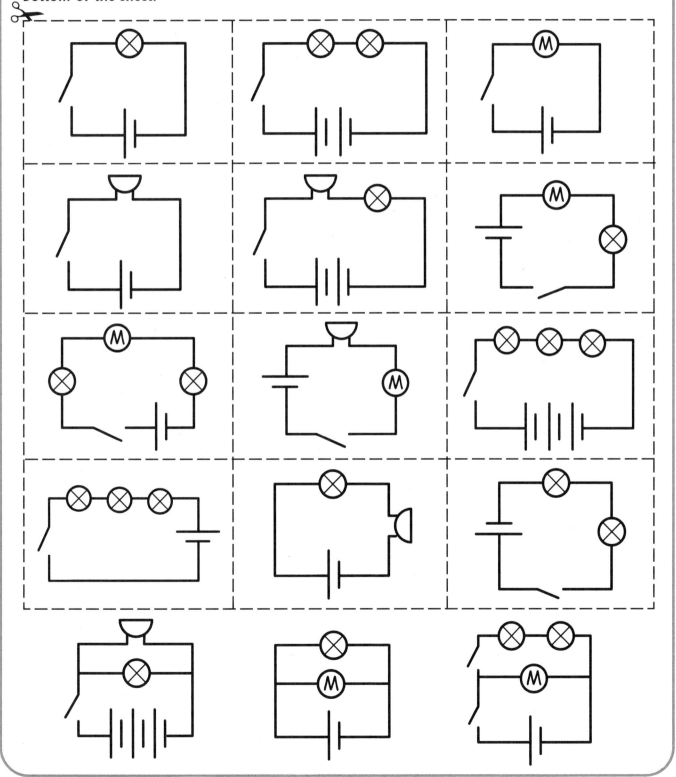

More circuit diagrams

Rewrite these sentences, matching each sentence starter with the correct ending.

The symbol for a bulb	a circle with an M inside.
A motor is shown by	is made up of two lines, one longer than the other.
The symbol for a buzzer	is a circle with a cross inside.
The symbol for a battery	even if the actual circuit is not rectangular.
A switch symbol	is this shape:
We always use the same symbols	looks like this:
Circuit diagrams are usually a rectangle shape	you should use a ruler.
A wire	is just shown by a straight line.
When you draw a circuit	to make circuit diagrams easy to read.

Conductors and insulators

Materials that let **electricity** pass through them easily are called **electrical conductors**. Wires that carry electricity from the **sockets** in your house to electrical equipment are made of **metal**. Metal lets the electricity pass through easily. It is a good conductor. Most good conductors are metals. Some other materials also conduct electricity, such as water and the **graphite** in pencils.

Electricity can be dangerous. If you touch a **bare wire**, you can get an **electric shock**. This is why the wires to electrical equipment are covered with **plastic**. The plastic will not let the electricity pass through, so it protects us. The plastic is an **electrical insulator**. Electrical insulators do not let electricity pass through easily.

Bob Bodger was an electrician. He was not a very good electrician. Look at this bill, which he sent to one of his customers.

Bob Bodger
Electrical Services

Item	Work done	Price
12 balls string	to rewire the house	£ 2.50
1 roll kitchen foil	to cover wires to make them safe	£ 1.22
50 lolly sticks	to make new plug pins	£ 0.99
Labour		£250.00
	TOTAL	£254.71

Bob Bodger's customers refused to pay his bills, because none of their electrical equipment worked when Bob had finished.

Conductors and insulators

1. What are materials that let electricity through easily known as?

_____

2. What does the electricity pass along to get from a socket to a

TV set? _____

3. What are wires made from? _____

4. Why are wires made from this?_____

_____

5. Why are wires covered with plastic?_____

_____

6. Why was string useless to Bob Bodger when he rewired his

customer's house?_____

_____

7. Why would electrical wires covered in kitchen foil be unsafe?

_____

_____

8. Why wouldn't lolly sticks be any use for
making the pins of electrical plugs?

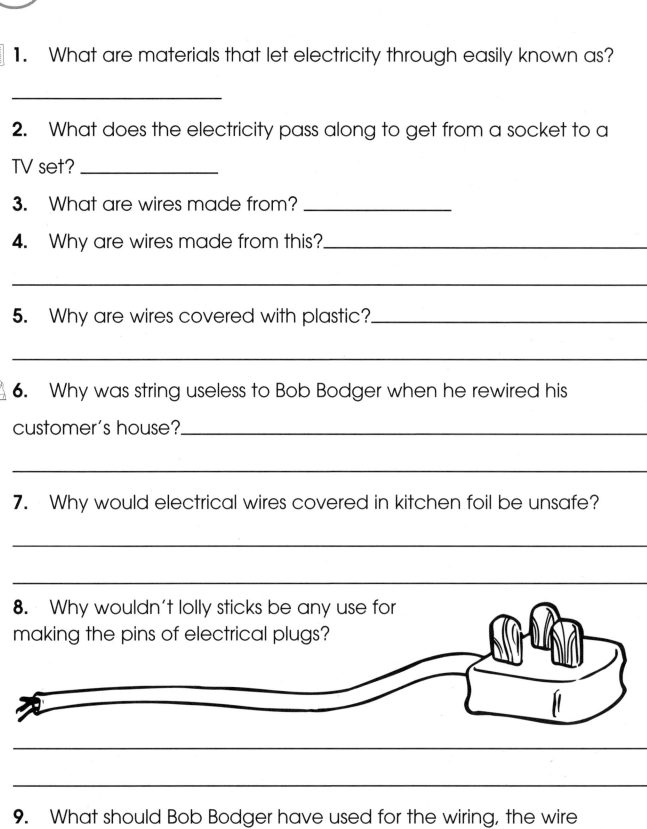

_____

_____

9. What should Bob Bodger have used for the wiring, the wire

covering and the plug pins?_____

_____

Write a letter to Bob Bodger to complain about his work.

Conductors and insulators

Tick the correct box.

1. A material that lets electricity through easily is called

an electrical insulator ☐

an electrical conductor ☐

2. Electricity gets from the sockets in your house to the television

through the air ☐

through string ☐

through wires ☐

3. Wires are made from metal because

it doesn't let electricity through ☐

it's a good electrical conductor ☐

4. Electrical wires are covered with

string ☐   plastic ☐   fabric ☐   kitchen foil ☐

5. Plastic is a good electrical   conductor ☐   insulator ☐

6. What did Bob Bodger use to rewire his customer's house?

_____

7. Why was that no good?_____

_____

8. Why would electrical wires covered in kitchen foil be unsafe?

_____

_____

9. What did Bob Bodger use for making plug pins? _____

10. Was that a good idea? _____

Write a letter to Bob Bodger to complain about his work.

Testing conductors and insulators

A group of pupils were testing circuits. They used a variety of everyday objects in their circuits. Some of these objects were electrical conductors and some were electrical insulators.

Look at the pictures and write **conductor** or **insulator** beside each object. Colour the bulbs that you think would have lit up.

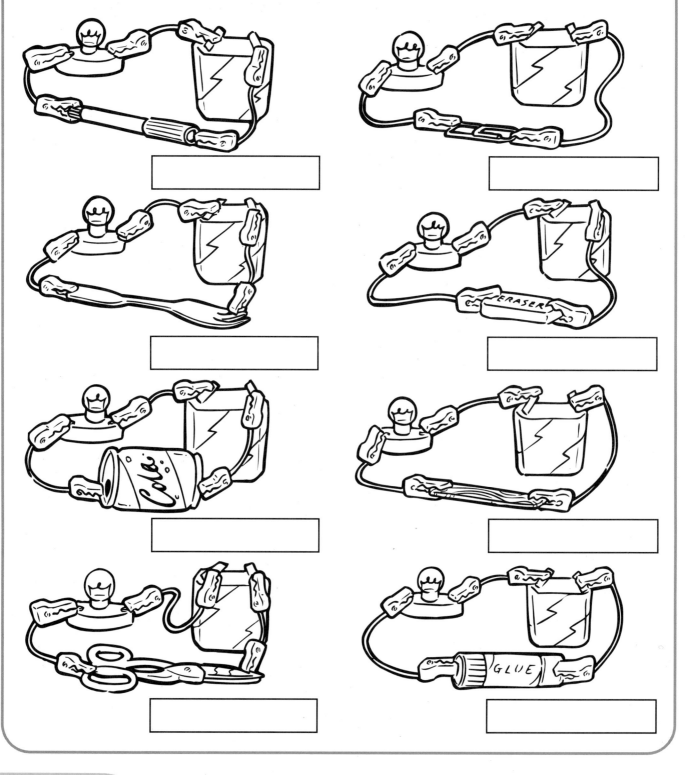

Conductor or insulator?

Cut out the labels and the pictures. Stick the pictures onto paper or into your science book, then stick a label beside each picture.

| conductor |
| insulator |
| conductor |
| insulator |
| conductor |
| insulator |
| conductor |
| insulator |
| conductor |
| insulator |
| conductor |
| insulator |
| conductor |
| insulator |
| conductor |
| insulator |

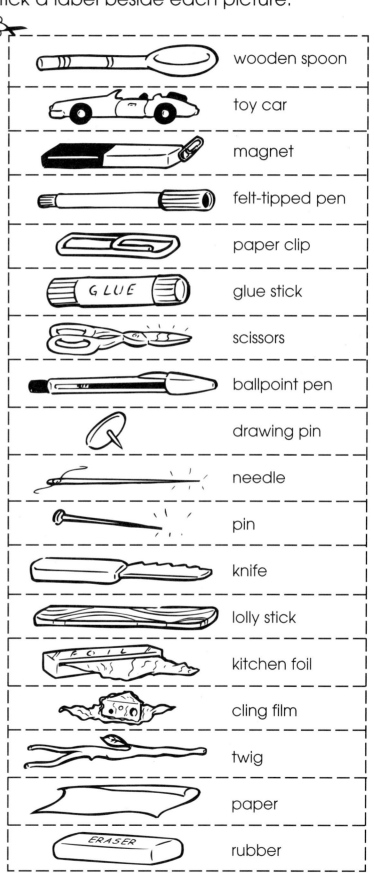

	wooden spoon
	toy car
	magnet
	felt-tipped pen
	paper clip
	glue stick
	scissors
	ballpoint pen
	drawing pin
	needle
	pin
	knife
	lolly stick
	kitchen foil
	cling film
	twig
	paper
	rubber

Beginnings and endings

Cut out the labels. Match the sentence beginnings to the correct endings and stick each pair together. Then decide on the best order for the sentences and stick them down on paper.

Most non-metals are	made from metal.
Some non-metals	is graphite.
This is why you should never touch a socket	string-pull switches.
If you connect the graphite in a pencil in a circuit	pencils.
That is why switches in bathrooms are usually	an electric shock.
A non-metal that conducts electricity well	poor electrical conductors.
Good electrical conductors are often	can conduct electricity well.
Another non-metal that conducts electricity	it will conduct electricity.
Graphite is used in	well is water.
The water on your hands could cause you to get	with wet hands.

Magnetic and non-magnetic

Think about all the rubbish you throw away each week. Most of it ends up in huge rubbish dumps.

In some parts of the country, each house has two bins for rubbish. One bin is for rubbish that can be recycled. The other bin is for rubbish that the local authorities do not recycle. **Metal**, **plastic**, **paper** and **glass** are some of the materials that can be recycled. When this rubbish is collected, it goes to a depot to be sorted. Some of the metal is **pulled** out by a giant **magnet**.

Iron and **steel** can be **separated** from the other rubbish because they are **attracted** to a magnet. We call these metals **magnetic**. Many food cans are made from these metals. Not all metals are magnetic. Many drinks cans are made from **aluminium**, which is **non-magnetic**.

The rest of the rubbish for recycling has to be sorted by hand, because the non-magnetic materials are not attracted by the pulling **force** of the giant magnet. Plastic, glass and paper are all non-magnetic.

Magnetic and non-magnetic

1. What materials that are mentioned in the text can be recycled?

   _____   _____   _____   _____

2. How is some of the rubbish separated from the rest?

   _____

3. Which common metals are attracted by a magnet?

   _____

4. What do we call materials that are attracted to a magnet?

   _____

5. Name a non-magnetic metal. _____

6. Circle the correct word:

   Magnetic materials are attracted to a magnet because of its

   pulling / pushing force.

7. Why does the rest of the rubbish for recycling have to be sorted by

   hand? _____

   _____

8. Write a list of some **objects** you know that are magnetic.

   _____

   _____

9. What must all of these objects have been made from?

   _____

10. Write a list of at least eight **materials** you know that are non-

    magnetic. _____

    _____

Imagine that you work in a recycling depot. Write a diary of your day
in the depot. Say which are the best and worst parts of the job.

Magnetic and non-magnetic

Fill in the blanks or circle the correct word.

1. Write down the names of four materials that can be recycled.

_____ _____ _____ _____

2. The rubbish goes to a depot to be _____.

3. How is some of the rubbish separated from the rest?

_____

4. Which two metals will stick to a magnet?

_____ and _____

5. Metals that stick to a magnet are **magnetic / non-magnetic**.

6. Some metals are pulled towards a magnet. We say that they are **detracted / attracted** by the magnet.

7. Some metals don't stick to magnets. These metals are **magnetic / non-magnetic**.

8. An example of a non-magnetic metal is _____

9. Why does the rest of the rubbish have to be sorted by hand?

_____

_____

10. What other materials do you know that are non-magnetic?

_____

_____

Imagine that you work in a recycling depot. Write a diary of your day in the depot. Say which are the best and worst parts of the job.

What material is it?

Cut out the pictures and labels. Match them up. Each picture needs three labels. Stick them onto a large sheet of paper.

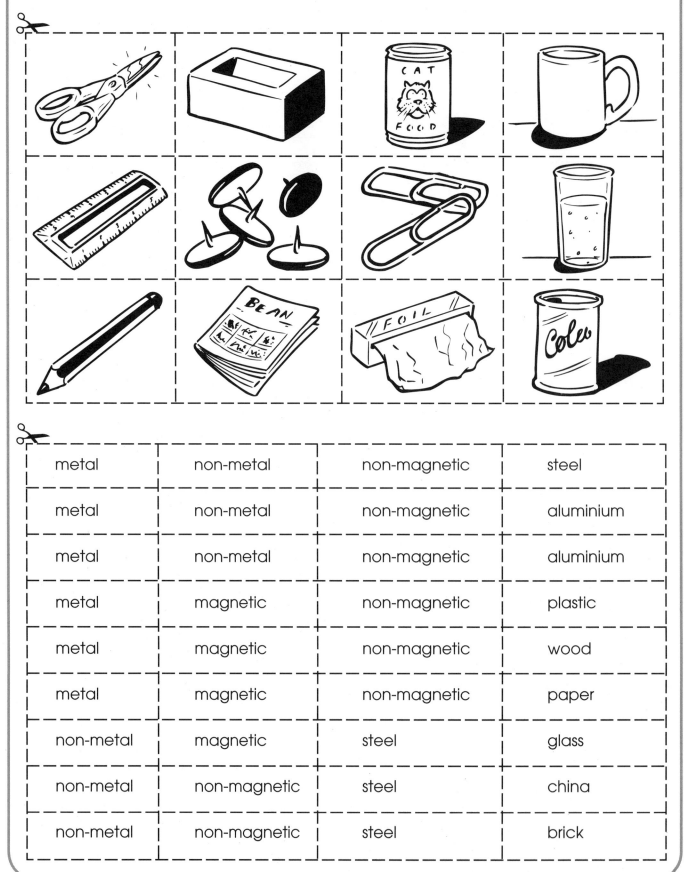

metal	non-metal	non-magnetic	steel
metal	non-metal	non-magnetic	aluminium
metal	non-metal	non-magnetic	aluminium
metal	magnetic	non-magnetic	plastic
metal	magnetic	non-magnetic	wood
metal	magnetic	non-magnetic	paper
non-metal	magnetic	steel	glass
non-metal	non-magnetic	steel	china
non-metal	non-magnetic	steel	brick

DEVELOPING SCIENCE LANGUAGE for Physical Processes with 8–9 year olds

Magnetic or non-magnetic?

Debbie is testing different items to find out whether they are magnetic or non-magnetic. Write captions to go with the pictures. You can use some of the words in the box below to help you.

_____

_____

_____

_____

_____

_____

_____

_____

_____

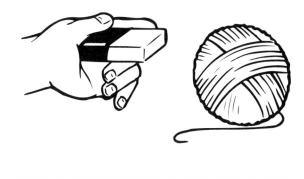

_____

_____

_____

drawing pins	pencil	wood
metal	iron	scissors
string	paper	separate
non-metal	steel	attract
paper clips	ruler	stick
magnetic	plastic	pull
bulldog clip	compass	cotton
non-magnetic	aluminium	force

_____

_____

_____

True or false?

Write true or false beside each sentence.

Magnets can be made from plastic.   _____

Magnets attract iron and steel.   _____

Magnets attract aluminium.   _____

All metals are magnetic.   _____

All non-metals are magnetic.   _____

Magnetic materials are pulled by a magnet.   _____

Non-magnetic materials are pushed by a magnet.   _____

Plastic-covered paper clips are not attracted to a magnet.   _____

Magnets can be used to sort out rubbish.   _____

Magnets stick to a fridge because of special paint on the
fridge door.   _____

Write two true sentences of your own about magnets and materials.

_____

_____

Now write one sentence that is false.

_____

Magnets, pushes and pulls

Here is what two groups of children wrote after they used magnets in their science lesson.

We were making **magnets** spin around. We floated a magnet in a bowl of water on top of a piece of polystyrene. We used another magnet to make the floating magnet spin. When we pointed **unlike poles** of the magnets at each other, the two magnets stuck together because they **attracted** each other. When we pointed **like poles** of the magnets at each other, the floating magnet started to spin because it was **repelled** by the other magnet.

Sadia
Zak
Alice

We made a **magnetic** theatre. We made card people with **magnets** stuck on their feet. We made the stage from card. To move the people, we used magnets stuck to sticks under the stage. We could pull the people along because the magnets

Janet
Jon
Freya

attracted each other. The **magnetic force** worked through the stage. If we turned our sticks over, the people moved away from the sticks because the magnets were **repelling** each other. We made more card people but we had run out of magnets, so we stuck paper clips to their feet instead. These were also attracted to the magnets under the stage because the paper clips were **magnetic**. We stuck kitchen foil to the feet of some other card people, but that did not work.

Magnets, pushes and pulls

1. What happened when Sadia, Zak and Alice pointed the unlike poles of the magnets at each other? Why did that happen?

_____ because _____

_____

2. When they pointed the like poles of the magnet at each other, why did the floating magnet start to spin?

_____

3. Explain how Janet, Jon and Freya could pull the card people across the stage in their magnetic theatre.

_____

_____

_____

4. What material did the magnetic force work through?

_____

5. Explain how they made the card people move away from the magnets underneath the stage.

_____

_____

_____

6. Why did they stick paper clips to the feet of the card people

when they ran out of magnets? _____

_____

7. Why was the kitchen foil not a good material to use?

_____

Write instructions for Sadia, Zak and Alice's experiment so that someone in your class could try it out.

Magnets, pushes and pulls

1. What were Sadia, Zak and Alice doing?

_____

2. The poles of a magnet are its ends. If you put unlike poles together, what happens? Tick the correct box.

The magnets pull on each other – they attract. ⬜

The magnets push on each other – they repel. ⬜

3. How did Sadia, Zak and Alice make the floating magnet spin?

_____

4. When you point like poles of two magnets together, they **attract / repel** each other. (Circle the correct word.)

5. Janet, Jon and Freya made a magnetic theatre.

What were the people made from? _____

What did they stick to the feet of the people? _____

What was the stage made from? _____

How did they make the people move? _____

_____

6. Some of the card people had paper clips stuck underneath. These

worked because the paper clips were _____

7. Why didn't the card people with kitchen foil stuck underneath

work? _____

Write instructions for Sadia, Zak and Alice's experiment so that someone in your class could try it out. Your teacher may give you some sentence starters to help you.

Pulling strength

Here are some instructions on how to test the strength of magnets. Put the instructions in the correct order and match them to the diagrams. Your teacher will tell you whether to number them or cut them out.

Put the squared paper on the table. Draw a line across one end. Put the paper clip behind the line.	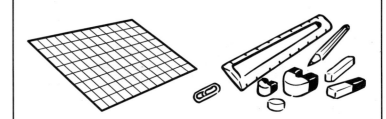
Put the paper clip behind the line again and test a different magnet.	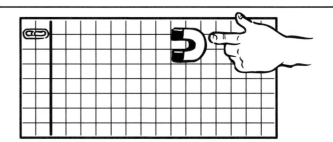
Put the magnet at the other end of the paper and push it slowly towards the paper clip.	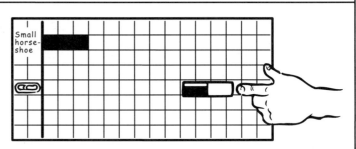
You will need: a piece of squared paper, a ruler, a pencil, a crayon, magnets, a paper clip.	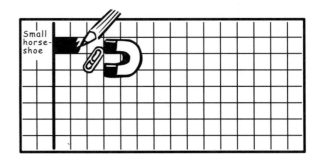
Stop pushing when the paper clip is attracted to the magnet. Colour the squares to show how far the paper clip moved, and write down which magnet you used.	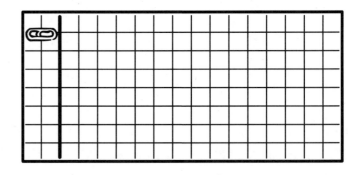

Magnetic attraction

Draw lines to match each picture with the correct label.

The tin is made from steel, so the magnet is attracted to it.

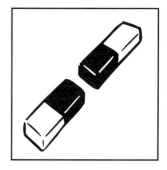

The plastic bottle is non-magnetic.

Iron nails are magnetic.

These magnets are pushing each other, because like poles repel each other.

The magnets are stuck together, because unlike poles attract each other.

The can is made from aluminium, so it does not stick to the magnet.

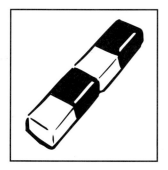

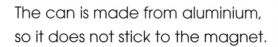

The pulling force from the magnet will make the paper clip move.

Not all metals are magnetic. The foil is not attracted to the magnet.

Magnets, pushes and pulls concept map

On the diagram below, find two words that are linked and draw a line between them. Write on the line why you have joined those words. One example has already been done for you.

Now join together as many pairs of words as you can. Each time, write on the line why you have joined them. You can use each word more than once.

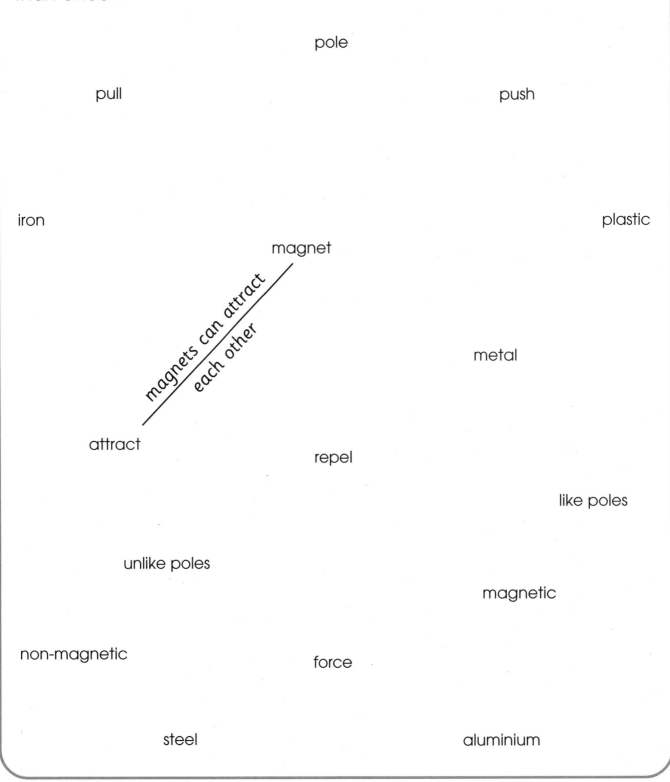

pole

pull

push

iron

plastic

magnet

magnets can attract each other

metal

attract

repel

like poles

unlike poles

magnetic

non-magnetic

force

steel

aluminium

Friction

Friction is a **force** that **slows** things down, or prevents them from starting to move. Sometimes friction is useful and sometimes it is not.

When you are up a ladder, the friction between the ladder and the ground stops the ladder slipping and falling down. This is useful friction.

If you are coming down a slide and someone has left chewing gum on it, it makes you **stick**! This is because of friction too, but this time it is not useful – and it's messy!

The **smoother** the **surface** of a slide, the **less** friction there is. This is why slides are often made from **polished** metal. The **rougher** the surface, the **more** friction there is. If you want to slow yourself down on a slide, you can put your feet down. The rough soles of your shoes make more friction, and that slows you down. If you want to **speed up**, you can sit on a sack to keep your feet off the slide. Then there will be less friction.

Friction

1. What two things can friction do? _____

    _____

2. Where might friction be useful? _____

    _____

    Where might friction not be useful? _____

    _____

3. Complete these sentences.

    The smoother the surface, _____

    The rougher the surface, _____

4. Describe how you could slow yourself down on a slide.

    _____

    _____

5. Write a list of things that can be slowed down by friction.

    ● A bike – by putting the brakes on.

    ● _____

    ● _____

    ● _____

    ● _____

Think about rollerblading on a wet day or playing football on a muddy field. Explain why the water or mud makes it more difficult. Use the word **friction** in your explanation.

Friction

1. Friction can _____ things down. It can also _____ things from starting to move. (Fill in the blanks.)

2. Draw lines to match the sentence starters with the correct endings.

    At the bottom of a ladder...   friction is not useful.

    On a slide...   friction is useful.

3. Complete these sentences.

    The smoother the surface... _____

    The rougher the surface... _____

4. Describe how you could slow yourself down on a slide.

    _____

    _____

5. Write a list of things that can be slowed down by friction.

    ● A bike – by putting the brakes on.

    ● _____

    ● _____

    ● _____

    ● _____

Think about rollerblading on a wet day or playing football on a muddy field. Explain why the water or mud makes it more difficult. Make sure you use the word **friction** in your explanation.

Testing shoes

You will need some coloured pencils for this activity.

A group of pupils tested some shoes to find out which one had the best grip. The report they wrote is shown below. Their report is not very clearly written.

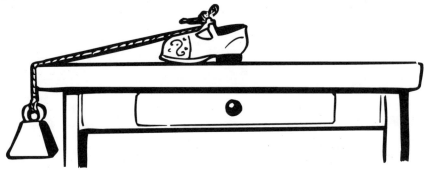

Underline the sentences that say what they **did** in **blue**.
Underline the sentences about how they made their experiment a **fair test** in **red**.
Underline their **observations** (what **happened**) in **green**.
Underline their **explanations** in **yellow**.

We were testing shoes to see which one had the best grip. First of all we put a shoe on the table and tied a piece of string to it. We hung the string over the edge of the table and added masses to it. How much mass we needed to add to make the shoe move showed how good the grip was. We used the same piece of string each time and put each shoe in the same place on the table. The gym shoe was best. It took 1kg to move it. It had grips made from rubber, which made a lot of friction with the table. The trainer was not very good. It only took 400g to move it. It did not make as much friction as we expected. We think the grips were worn out. We made sure we did not pull on the string. That would have been cheating!

DEVELOPING SCIENCE LANGUAGE for Physical Processes with 8–9 year olds

Testing shoes

Here is the graph that the pupils drew after they had tested the different shoes.

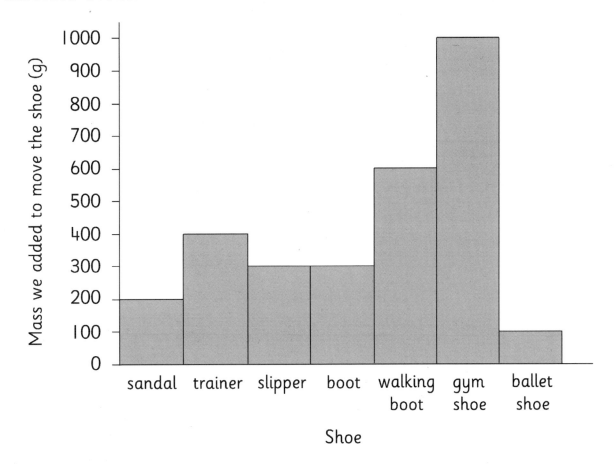

Write a list of questions that this graph answers. Here are some starters:

1. Which shoe had the best grip?

2. Which shoe… _____

3. What mass was needed… _____

4. Which three shoes… _____

5. How many shoes… _____

6. _____

7. _____

8. _____

9. _____

10. _____

Increasing friction

Describe and explain what happens each time. Use the word **friction**.

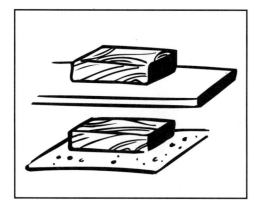

Push a block of wood along on a table. Now put it on a sheet of sandpaper and try to push it along the table on the sandpaper.

_____

_____

_____

Try to unscrew the cap of a pop bottle. Now put on a rubber glove and try again.

_____

_____

_____

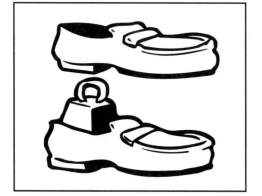

Slide a shoe across the floor. Put a 1kg mass inside the shoe and try to slide it again.

_____

_____

_____

Push a toy car across a tiled floor. Now try to push it across a carpet.

_____

_____

_____

Reducing friction

Describe and explain what happens each time. Use the word **friction**.

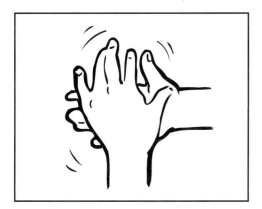

Rub your hands together. Put on some hand cream, then rub your hands together again.

_____

_____

_____

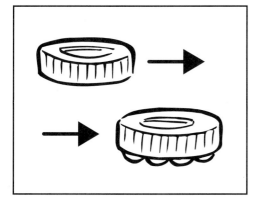

Push the lid from a jar across a table. Put some marbles under the lid and push it again.

_____

_____

_____

Pick up some marbles. Now rub some cooking oil into your hands and try to pick up the marbles again.

_____

_____

_____

Pick up a full plastic bottle of pop. Put the bottle in the sink. Wet your hands and the bottle, then try to pick it up again.

_____

_____

_____

Friction – useful or not?

Draw a table like this on a sheet of A4 paper:

Friction is not useful here	Friction is useful here

Cut out the examples below and stick them in the correct places on the table. Add some of your own.

✂

Friction at the bottom of a ladder stops it moving.	If you do not oil the chain on a bike, it will be hard to turn the pedals.	If ice skaters' blades are not sharp, it slows them down.
Bike brakes are made from rubber. They press against the wheels to slow them down.	Skiers put wax on their skis to make them slide easily over the snow.	Rock climbers put chalk on their hands to give them a good grip.
Slides in swimming pools have water running down them.	Walking boots have rubber soles with deep grips to stop you slipping.	If you can't unscrew a bottle top, wearing a rubber glove can sometimes help you to grip it better.

DEVELOPING SCIENCE LANGUAGE for Physical Processes with 8–9 year olds

Vibrations

When an object makes a **sound**, it **vibrates**. This means that it makes very tiny **movements**. If you put your hand on your throat and groan or hum, you can feel your **voice box** vibrating.

URGH!

Sometimes you can actually see an object **vibrating**. If you hold a ruler on the edge of the table and 'twang' it, you can see it moving. The **harder** you twang it, the more it vibrates and the **louder** the sound. If you twang it more gently, the sound is **quieter**. The smaller the vibrations, the quieter the sound.

Sometimes an object making a sound vibrates so quickly that it's difficult to see the **vibrations**. If you strike a **tuning fork**, the vibrations are difficult to see. You can see them better if you put the prongs of the tuning fork in water, so that the vibration of the prongs makes the water vibrate.

If you bang a drum, it's difficult to see the drum skin vibrate. If you put rice on top of the drum, the vibrations will make the rice jump about.

In different musical instruments, different parts vibrate. The strings of a stringed instrument and the skins or walls of percussion instruments vibrate, but in a wind instrument the air inside is vibrating.

Vibrations

1. How are sounds made? _____

_____

2. List three things that vibrate to make a sound.

_____

3. Complete these sentences.
   The smaller the vibrations, _____
   The bigger the vibrations, _____

4. Give two examples of ways we can make vibrations easier to see.

_____

_____

_____

_____

5. Draw a table on the back of this sheet to show twelve instruments and the part of each instrument that vibrates.

Evelyn Glennie is a famous musician. Use this information to make a factfile about her.

Evelyn Glennie began to lose her hearing when she was eight years old, and was almost completely deaf by the age of twelve. Since then, she has learned to play all kinds of percussion instruments. She cannot hear them well, so she has to feel the vibrations through her feet and body. Evelyn plays in concerts all over the world. When she travels, she takes 20 to 50 instruments with her. She also writes her own music, and works together with her husband to write music for films.

Try searching for Evelyn Glennie on the Internet for more information.

Vibrations

1. When an object makes a sound, what does it do?

_____

2. What is vibration? _____

_____

3. When you groan or hum, what is vibrating?

_____

4. Give an example of something that makes a noise where you can see the vibrations.

_____

5. If you make something vibrate harder, the sound becomes **louder / softer**. (Circle the correct word.)

_____

6. Complete this sentence.

The smaller the vibrations, _____

7. How can you tell that a drum skin is vibrating?

_____

_____

Evelyn Glennie is a famous musician. Use this information to make a factfile about her.

Evelyn Glennie began to lose her hearing when she was eight years old, and was almost completely deaf by the age of twelve. Since then, she has learned to play all kinds of percussion instruments. She cannot hear them well, so she has to feel the vibrations through her feet and body. Evelyn plays in concerts all over the world. When she travels, she takes 20 to 50 instruments with her. She also writes her own music, and works together with her husband to write music for films.

Try searching for Evelyn Glennie on the Internet for more information.

Ping-pong balls and tuning forks

Here is a way of making vibrations easier to see.

1. Attach a piece of string to a ping-pong ball with sticky tape.

2. Hold the ping-pong ball by the string.

3. Bang the prongs of a tuning fork.

4. Quickly touch the dangling ping-pong ball with the tuning fork.

5. The vibration of the tuning fork should make the ball jump away.

Use these instructions to write an experiment report. Your teacher may give you some sentence starters to help you.

Question _____

Apparatus _____

_____

Method (what we did)	Diagram
_____	
_____	
_____	
_____	
_____	
_____	
_____	

Observations (what we saw) _____

_____

Conclusions (explanation) _____

_____

Vibrations make sounds

Next to each picture, write a few sentences to describe and explain what is happening. Use the words in the box to help you.

_____

_____

_____

_____

_____

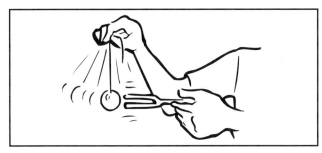

_____

_____

_____

_____

_____

_____

_____

_____

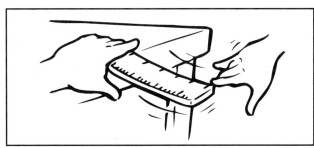

_____

_____

_____

_____

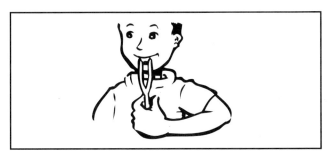

tuning fork	drum	vibrations	pluck	bang
ping-pong ball	feel	twang	guitar	ruler
rice	loud	soft	small	large	quiet	vibrate

Sound and vibrations card game

Teacher instructions

Photocopy onto card. Cut along the dotted lines. Fold each card in half along the solid line, with the text on the outside, and fasten with adhesive tape.

If you are working with a small group, give each child a card. If you are working with the whole class, share the cards out one between two or three. All the cards must be given out.

The child (or group) with the card marked * reads the sentence starter aloud. The child (or group) with the correct ending to that sentence reads it out, then reads out the starter on the back. This goes on until the first child (or group) has read out the ending on the first card.

fold

* When an object vibrates	can make a ping-pong ball jump.
In a stringed instrument	it makes a sound.
Vibrations are not always	the strings vibrate.
The smaller the vibrations,	easy to see.
A loud sound is caused	the quieter the sound.
To see a tuning fork vibrate,	by large vibrations.
In a drum	place the prongs in water.
To see a drum skin vibrate,	the drum skin vibrates.
Vibrations are	put some rice on the drum.
The bigger the vibrations,	very tiny movements.
When you groan	the louder the sound.
If you blow into a wind instrument	you can feel your voice box vibrate.
Soft sounds are caused by	the air inside it vibrates.
You can feel a tuning fork vibrate	small vibrations.
A tuning fork vibrating	if you hold it gently on your face.

Sounds travelling

Sounds can **travel** through **solids**, **liquids** and **gases**. If you **listen** to the sound made by tapping a pencil on a table, the sound travels to your **ears** through the **air**. The air is a mixture of gases. If you put your ear to the table and tap again, the tapping sounds much **louder**. This time, the sound is travelling through the solid table. In a string telephone, the sound travels down the stretched string. The string is a solid.

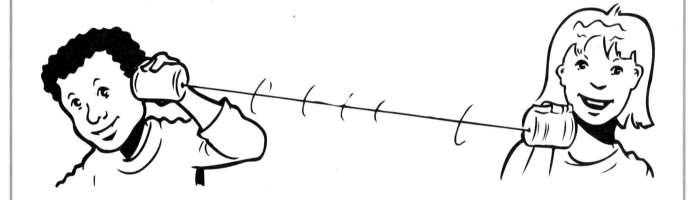

Sounds travel through liquids too. If you are swimming underwater in a swimming pool, the noises around the pool still reach your ears. If you hold a balloon filled with air to your ear and hold a ticking watch on the other side of the balloon, you can hear the tick – but if you try again using a balloon filled with water, the tick will sound louder. Sounds travel better through solids and liquids than through gases.

How can we prove that sounds travel through gases? If you put rice on a drum and then bang a second drum close by, the rice on the first drum jumps about because of the **vibrations** passing through the air from the second drum.

Sounds travelling

1. Describe three tests to show that sounds travel through solids, liquids and gases.

Solids _____

_____

Liquids _____

_____

Gases _____

_____

2. When sounds travel through solids, how do they sound?

_____

3. Do sounds travel better through gases or through solids and liquids?

_____

4. Why does rice on a drum move about when another drum close

by is banged? _____

_____

5. Explain how the sound travels in each of these drawings.

_____   _____

_____   _____

Write down four key points that summarise the information on the 'Sounds travelling' sheet.

Sounds travelling

1. What three types of material can sounds travel through?

   _____

2. How can you tell that sounds travel through solids?

   _____

   _____

3. How could you show that sounds travel through liquids?

   _____

   _____

4. When you put your ear to a table and listen to a pencil tapping on
the table, how does it sound? _____

   _____

5. Do sounds travel better through gases or through solids and liquids?

   _____

6. Why does rice on a drum move about when another drum close
by is banged? _____

   _____

7. Label these diagrams with **solid, liquid** and **gas** to show what the
sound is travelling through.

Write down four key points that summarise the information on the
'Sounds travelling' sheet.

Advantages and disadvantages

Look at these statements about sounds travelling. Decide whether they are advantages or disadvantages, and write each number in the correct column in the table below.

1. If I am swimming underwater, I can still hear the sports centre fire alarm because sounds travel through liquids.

2. I can hear my neighbours arguing next door, because the sound travels through the solid wall next to my bed.

3. The people in the flat above play their stereo very loudly. I can hear it through the solid floor.

4. If I move about in my bedroom after bedtime, my mum can tell because she can hear me through the ceiling.

5. Some men are drilling the road outside. My dad is on night shifts, so it is keeping him awake.

6. I can tell if there's someone behind me in the subway, because the sound echoes around in the enclosed space.

7. We do not always hear the bell for break in our classroom, because we are a long way from where the bell rings.

8. My dog barks when he hears footsteps on the front path.

Advantages	Disadvantages

Now add some statements of your own to each column in the table.

Sounds travelling through solids

Here are the reports that two groups of pupils wrote about experiments they carried out in science.

Sounds travelling through solids

We tied a fork to the middle of a 50cm string. We pressed the string to our ears. Then we let the fork swing and bang against the table. The sound we heard was very loud because it travelled through the solid string to our ears.

Alison and Barbara

Sounds travelling through solids

Our group used rubber bands of different thicknesses to make sounds. We pressed the bands to our ears, so our ears were 'closed'. Then we stretched the bands and twanged them. The sounds were loud. We made the sounds change by stretching the bands more.

Adrienne, Chris and Damira

Write instructions to explain to other groups of pupils how to carry out the same two activities.

Sounds travelling through metal and string

Sounds travelling through rubber bands

Sound information book

You need: 'Sound information book (2)', enlarged to A3 size if possible; scissors.

1. Fold the sheet in half.

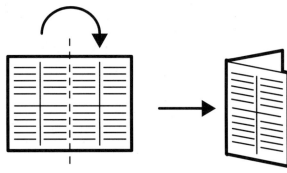

2. Fold it in half again.

3. Fold it in half again.

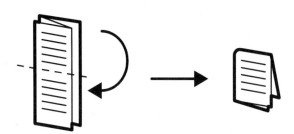

4. Open it out and fold it like this:

5. Cut from the fold to the bottom.

6. Open the sheet like this:

7. Fold it up so the title is on the front.

8. Look at each heading in the book you have made. Write a few sentences under each heading and add illustrations.

Sound information book

2

Making sounds	Sound information book Name: _____
Vibrations	Words to describe sounds
Loud and quiet	Hearing
Musical instruments	Sounds travelling

A sound story

Annie is making a noise by squeezing a squeaky toy inside a plastic bag underwater. Explain how the sound is made, how it travels to Catherine, and how Catherine hears the sound.

Use as many of these words as you can. You may use some of the words more than once.

squeeze	vibration	solid	liquid	gas
travels	direction air	vibrates	loud	quiet
source	ear	hear	sound	noise	water

_____

_____

_____

_____

_____

_____

_____

_____

_____

A light problem

Desmond was having trouble sleeping. This is a letter he wrote to his friend Denis, a scientist working in America, to ask him for some advice.

17 Smith Street
Leeds
England

10th June

Dear Denis,

How are you? I am fine, except that at my factory I am working on the **night** shift. I find it very difficult getting to sleep in the **day**. It's not the noise that bothers me, the kids are out at school most of the time. It's the **light**. It's very sunny at this time of year. Sometimes I try to sleep in my bed, but the curtains are thin, so the light can get through. They are made from **translucent** fabric. I am thinking about changing them. The ones in the kitchen are much thicker. They are **opaque**. The light doesn't get through at all – but I can't sleep in the kitchen sink, can I? I thought about sleeping in the kids' room, but they don't have curtains and the glass in the windows is **transparent**. You can see right through them. What do you think I should do?

All the best,

Des (sleepy!)

A light problem

 1. What is Desmond having trouble with? _____

2. Why can't he sleep in the day? _____

_____

3. What are the curtains like in Desmond's bedroom? **thick / thin**

4. What do these words mean?

transparent _____

translucent _____

opaque _____

5. Which of those words best describes Desmond's curtains?

_____

 6. Should Desmond choose new curtains? _____

What sort of material should he choose? _____

Why? _____

_____

 Write a list of materials. Say whether they are transparent, translucent or opaque (for example: bubble wrap – transparent, tracing paper – translucent, card – opaque).

A light problem

Answer these questions. You may need to fill a gap, tick the correct box or circle the correct answer.

1. What is Desmond having trouble with?

    _____

2. He can't sleep in the day, because of the _____

3. His curtains are **thick / thin**.

4. All day in Desmond's bedroom, it is _____

5. **Transparent** means   you can see through   ☐

                     light can get through   ☐

                     no light can get through   ☐

6. **Translucent** means   you can see through   ☐

                     light can get through   ☐

                     no light can get through   ☐

7. What does **opaque** mean? _____

8. Desmond's curtains are **transparent / translucent / opaque**.

9. Which type of material do you think would be the best for Desmond's curtains?

    Transparent ☐   Translucent ☐   Opaque ☐

    Why? _____

    _____

Write a list of materials. Say whether they are transparent, translucent or opaque (for example: bubble wrap – transparent, tracing paper – translucent, card – opaque).

Denis' experiment

Denis tested some different materials to see which would be best for his friend's new curtains. He has written a letter to Des about it.

Use the instructions on the next page to make an airmail letter. Stick or rewrite Denis' notes about his experiment in the right order on the letter.

Here are my results:

Material	Did the light shine through?	
clear plastic	yes	
thin cotton	a little	
towelling	a tiny bit, through little holes	
net		quite a lot
velvet		no

These results show that the clear plastic was transparent, the thin cotton and net were translucent, and the towelling was almost opaque. The velvet was completely opaque. No light could get through.

I shone a torch behind each piece of material. I looked to see whether the light was coming through at all.

Dear Des,

I wanted to find out the answer to your problem. Which would be the best material to make curtains from that will block out the light while you're trying to sleep in the daytime?

I used five different materials. They were clear plastic, thin cotton, towelling, net and velvet. I thought the towelling would be the best because it was the thickest.

The velvet was the best material for keeping the light out, because it was thick and didn't seem to have any tiny holes for the light to get through. It was opaque. I think you should change to velvet curtains.

Best wishes,

Denis

Making an airmail letter

You need: a sheet of A4 paper, scissors, adhesive.

1. Fold the sheet of paper in half along the dotted line.

2. Open it out and fold the sides into the middle.

3. Fold it almost in half along the dotted line.

 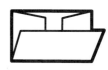

4. Cut off the top corners.

 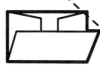 

5. Fold over the flaps.

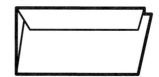

6. Open the sheet out and cut off the bits that are shaded on the picture.

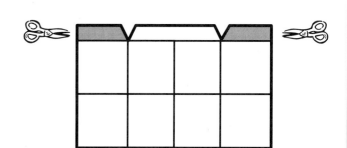

7. This is your airmail letter. Stick or rewrite Denis' notes about his experiment in the correct sections.

Dear Des	1	2	3
4	5	6	Hope it solves your problem, Denis.

Transparent, translucent and opaque

Use the instructions on the next page to make your own pyramid display book.

Cut out these pictures and stick them in the correct places on the pyramid display book. Add some pictures of your own.

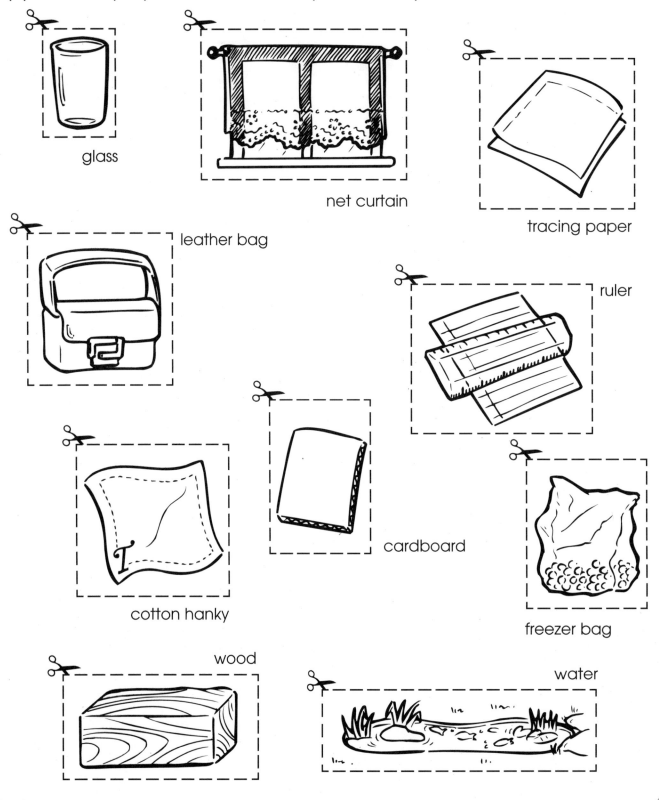

glass

net curtain

tracing paper

leather bag

ruler

cotton hanky

cardboard

freezer bag

wood

water

Making a pyramid display book

You need: a sheet of A3 paper, scissors, adhesive.

1. Fold a sheet of A3 paper like this: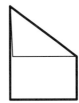

2. Cut off the end part.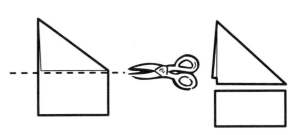

3. Open out the folded part and fold it again the opposite way.

4. Open it out again and cut one fold to the middle.

5. Fold the sheet like this: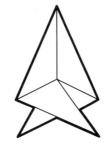

6. Write **transparent, translucent** and **opaque** on the sides.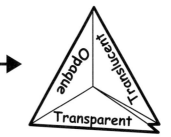

7. Stick the pictures from the other worksheet in the correct places.

Testing materials

A group of children have been given some equipment. They want to find the best material for making shadow puppets.

Use the words in the box to help you write instructions for the children.

Equipment

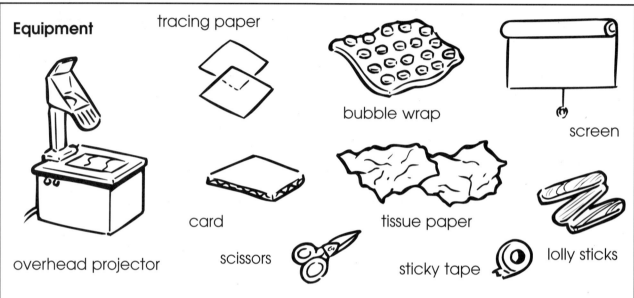

tracing paper

bubble wrap

screen

card

tissue paper

overhead projector

scissors

sticky tape

lolly sticks

shine	bright	shadow	switch	transparent
look	light	opaque	clear	dim	puppet
translucent	dark	position	fuzzy	best
record	table	results

1. First _____

2. Next _____

3. Then _____

4. _____

5. _____

_____

Making shadows

Some pupils were investigating **shadows**. They tried to make shadows with different **materials** by shining a **torch** at different **objects** to see what the shadows were like.

First they tried shining the torch through a glass. The glass was **transparent**. There did not seem to be a shadow at all, just a hazy outline. They could see clearly through the glass.

Then they tried shining the torch through the window of a doll's house. The **clear** plastic didn't make a shadow, but the wooden frame did.

Next, they tried a small piece of tracing paper. They could see light and shapes through the paper, but not clearly. It was **translucent**. It made a faint, fuzzy shadow. A piece of a thin, cotton hanky made a shadow like this too.

Next, they tried a piece of cardboard. The cardboard was **opaque**. They could not see through it. It made a **dark** shadow.

They found that opaque objects **block** the **light**, and this is how shadows are made. They collected opaque objects and materials. In their collection they had cardboard, a rubber, a pair of scissors, a pen, a book, a notepad, a plastic fork and a lolly stick.

Making shadows

1. What six materials did the children test?

_____

_____

2. The materials can be described by three words. What does each word mean?

transparent _____

translucent _____

opaque _____

3. Describe the shadow made by each type of material.

transparent _____

translucent _____

opaque _____

4. Explain how shadows are made.

_____

_____

Try to remember the biggest shadow you have seen. Describe the shadow and how it was made.

Making shadows

1. Draw lines to match these words to the correct meanings. There are two meanings for each word.

transparent

translucent

opaque

> light and shapes can be seen through it, but not clearly

> light and shapes cannot be seen through it

> light and shapes can be clearly seen through it

> it makes no shadows

> it makes dark shadows

> it makes fuzzy shadows

2. Copy the table below onto another sheet of paper. Write these names of objects in the correct columns in the table.

cardboard	blown-up balloon	glass	notepad
bubble wrap	wooden frame	tracing paper	pen
CD case	plastic fork	clear plastic window	
thin cotton hanky		frosted glass window	

transparent	translucent	opaque

3. Add two or three more things to each column in the table above.

4. Explain how shadows are made. _____

_____

Try to remember the biggest shadow you have seen. Describe the shadow and how it was made.

The biggest shadow I have ever seen

It was _____

It was so big because _____

_____

What would the shadow be like?

On each picture, draw the shadow and explain why the shadow would be that shape and size. Say whether the shadow would be sharp-edged or fuzzy. You may need to make the shadows to help you write your explanations.

_____
_____
_____
_____

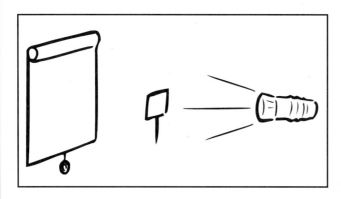

_____
_____
_____

_____
_____
_____

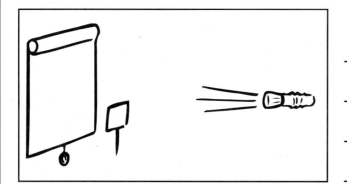

_____
_____
_____

What would the shadow be like?   2

Match the sentence starters to the correct endings.

The nearer you move the light to the object,	when the object is near to the screen.
The further you move the light away from the object,	the shadow will appear to have fuzzy edges.
Fuzzy shadows appear when	the smaller the shadow becomes.
Clear-edged shadows are made	the object is close to the light source.
If you use a small light source,	the larger the shadow becomes.
If you use a candle as your light source,	the shadow will be clear-edged.
If you use a large light source,	the shadow will move a little because the light source is flickering.

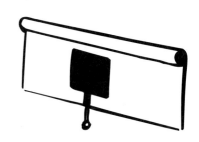

A shadows experiment

Some pupils started writing up their experiment on shadows, but they didn't have time to finish. Complete their work for them.

Question How can we make the biggest shadow?

Apparatus _____

_____

_____

Method	**Diagram**
_____	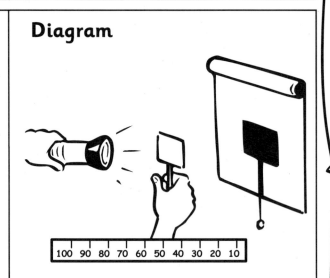
_____	
_____	
_____	
_____	
_____	100 90 80 70 60 50 40 30 20 10

Results

Distance of object from screen	Height_____
10cm	11cm
20cm	12cm
30cm	13cm
40cm	14cm
50cm	17cm
60cm	25cm
_____	33cm
_____	41cm
_____	67cm

Graph

Height of shadow (cm): 70 60 50 40 30 20 10 0

10 20 30

_____

Conclusion Our graph shows that the further _____

_____

The line on the graph went up gradually to begin with, then _____

_____

Objects and their shadows

Write a caption to go with each picture. Describe the object and its shadow, then explain why the shadow looks the way it does. You can use the words in the box to help you.

glass	shadow	transparent	faint	fuzzy	Sun
translucent	position	opaque	outline		sundial
direction	size	curtains	shape	large	angle
travels	net	light	block		straight

Making shadows concept map

On the diagram below, find two words that are linked and draw a line between them. Write on the line why you have joined those words. One example has already been done for you.

Now join together as many pairs of words as you can. Each time, write on the line why you have joined them. You can use each word more than once.

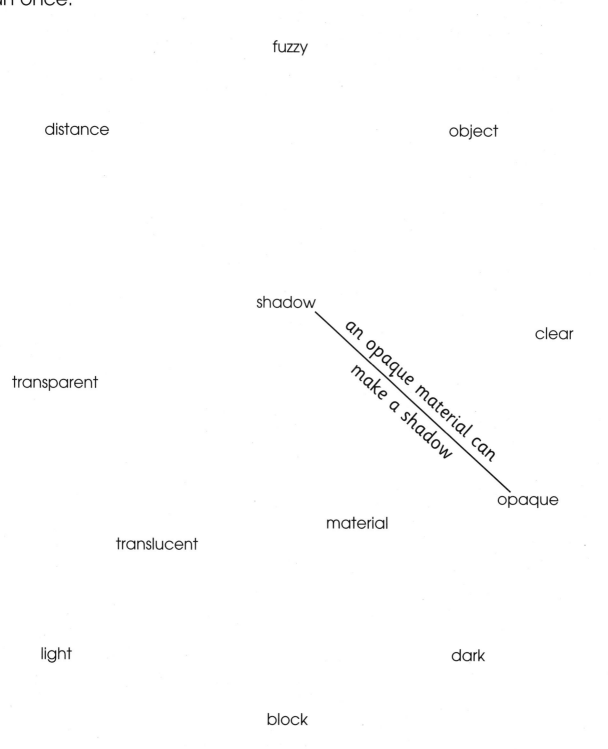

fuzzy

distance

object

shadow

clear

transparent

an opaque material can make a shadow

opaque

material

translucent

light

dark

block

DEVELOPING SCIENCE LANGUAGE for Physical Processes with 8–9 year olds

Shadows through the day

Here is a report written by a group of pupils who were observing shadows through the day.

Question What happens to **shadows** through the **day**?
Apparatus We used chalk, a compass and a metre ruler.

Method At different times during the day, we went outside and Heather stood in a fixed place in the playground. Each time, we drew around her shadow with chalk and measured its **length** and the **direction** the **Sun** was shining from.

Diagram

Observations

This is the pattern we observed:

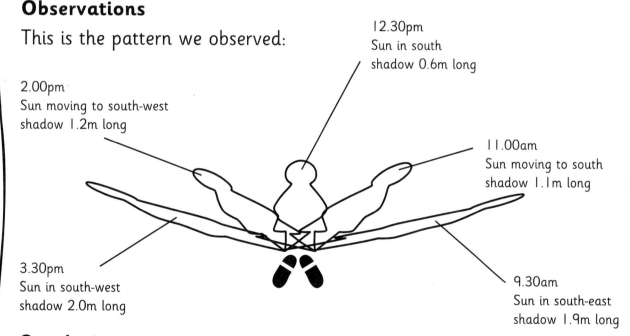

12.30pm
Sun in south
shadow 0.6m long

2.00pm
Sun moving to south-west
shadow 1.2m long

11.00am
Sun moving to south
shadow 1.1m long

3.30pm
Sun in south-west
shadow 2.0m long

9.30am
Sun in south-east
shadow 1.9m long

Conclusions

The shadow changes direction as the **position** of the Sun in the sky changes. It gets **shorter** as **midday** approaches, because the Sun is **higher** in the sky. As the Sun sets, the shadow gets **longer** again.

Shadows through the day

1. Write three instructions for the pupils' experiment.

● _____

● _____

● _____

2. Describe what happened to the length of Heather's shadow as the day passed.

_____

_____

_____

3. Describe the children's observations of the position of the shadow. Why did this happen?

_____

_____

_____

4. Complete these sentences.

● The lower the Sun, _____

● The higher the Sun, _____

● When the Sun is in the east, _____

● When the Sun is in the west, _____

5. How could you change the length of a shadow made by a stick, using a torch? _____

Write a list of adjectives to describe shadows. Use these words to create a poem about a shadow. Start each line of the poem with the letter shown.

S

H

A

D

O

W

Shadows through the day

1. Write three instructions for finding out what happens to shadows during the day.

- Stand _____

- Draw around _____

- Measure _____

2. What happened to the length of Heather's shadow?

At 9.30am it was _____

At 11.00am _____

By _____

Then _____

Finally _____

3. Did the shadow stay in the same position? _____

Explain what happened. _____

_____

4. What happens to the length of the shadow as the Sun gets higher in the sky? _____

5. Complete this sentence.

The lower the Sun, _____

6. How could you change the length of a shadow made by a stick, using a torch? _____

Write a list of adjectives to describe shadows. Use these words to create a poem about a shadow. Start each line of the poem with the letter shown.

S

H

A

D

O

W

Shadows, time and seasons

Before electricity was invented, people could not do much at night because they did not have enough light. They worked during the daylight hours, and used candles and gas lamps for light during the night.

During the summer, the daylight time is longer. During the winter, the days seem shorter because the dawn is later and the dusk is earlier. The Sun also appears to be lower in the sky. Shadows are longer in winter than in summer, and it is colder.

Thousands of years ago, before clocks were invented, people used the Sun to tell the time. They became familiar with the position of the Sun in the sky through the day. They could tell when it was about halfway through the day because the Sun was at its highest point. They knew when it was about to set, because it appeared to pass over to the west.

The Romans used sundials to tell the time more accurately. A sundial works by casting a shadow onto a type of clock face. As the Sun appears to change position in the sky, the shadow on the dial moves around.

Write a list of ten questions that this piece of text answers. For example:

In what part of the day did people work before electricity was invented?

Changing shadows

A group of pupils were given a set of cards telling and showing them how to change the length of a shadow. The cards became mixed up.

Cut out the cards. Put the instructions in the correct order, then match each one to the correct diagram.

Measure the length of the shadow.

Move the torch around the angle board another 10 degrees, then measure the length of the shadow.

Make an angle board by marking 10 degree intervals on the card, using the protractor.

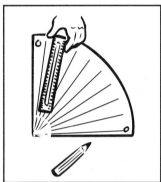

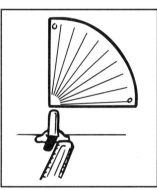

Repeat until the torch is shining horizontally at the lolly stick.

Hold the torch on the 10 degree mark above the lolly stick, level with the edge of the angle card.

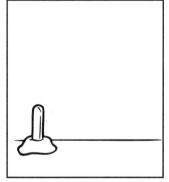

You will need: a torch, a protractor, a lolly stick, a ruler, Plasticine, a large piece of card the shape of a quarter circle, a tape measure.

Place the lolly stick upright in the Plasticine, a few centimetres from a wall.

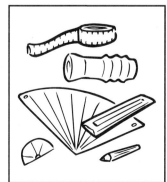

Fix the angle board to the wall, just behind the top of the lolly stick.

2 Changing shadows

A group of pupils carried out an experiment to find out what happened to the length of a shadow when they changed the angle of a torch to an object. Here are the diagram, table of results and graph they made.

Angle	Length of shadow	Angle	Length of shadow
10°	64cm	100°	3cm
20°	32cm	110°	6cm
30°	22cm	120°	9cm
40°	16cm	130°	12cm
50°	11cm	140°	16cm
60°	9cm	150°	23cm
70°	5cm	160°	34cm
80°	2cm	170°	67cm
90°	0cm		

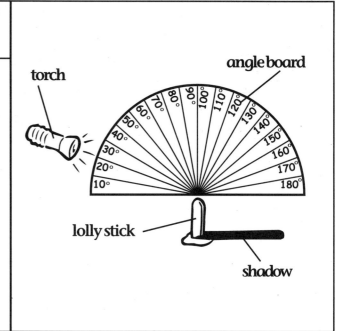

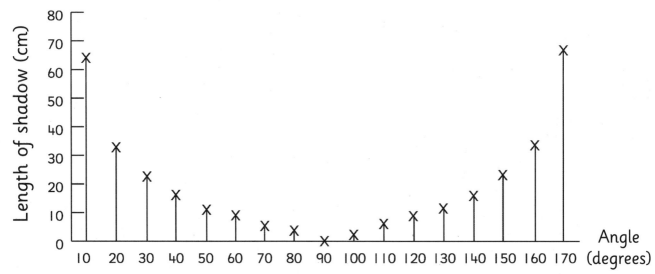

Write a list of questions that could be answered by the graph. Use these words to help you.

length	increases	long		longer
shadow		degrees	angle	shorter
decreases	shortest	short		longest

For example:

What angle is the torch pointing at when there is no shadow?

Shadows bingo sheet

Teacher instructions

Give out the bingo cards to groups of children. One child acts as caller and calls out the questions in random order. The children tick off the answers on their card. When a group of children have a line of four answers going across their card, they can call out 'House'.

transparent	translucent	opaque	highest
shadow	blocks	direction	lowest
light	Sun	shortest	longest

translucent	opaque	highest	shadow
blocks	direction	lowest	light
Sun	shortest	longest	transparent

opaque	highest	shadow	blocks
direction	lowest	light	Sun
shortest	longest	transparent	translucent

highest	shadow	blocks	direction
lowest	light	Sun	shortest
longest	transparent	translucent	opaque

transparent	shadow	light	translucent
blocks	Sun	opaque	direction
shortest	highest	lowest	longest

2 Shadows bingo sheet

shadow	light	translucent	blocks
Sun	opaque	direction	shortest
highest	lowest	longest	transparent

light	translucent	blocks	Sun
opaque	direction	shortest	highest
lowest	longest	transparent	shadow

translucent	blocks	Sun	opaque
direction	shortest	highest	lowest
longest	transparent	shadow	light

Question cards – cut out and keep in a box or bag.

Materials that you can see through are _____.	Materials that let a little bit of light through are _____.	Materials that block the light are _____.
Shadows are shortest when the Sun is at its _____ in the sky.	When an opaque object blocks the light, you see one of these.	A shadow is formed when an object _____ the light.
Shadows are longest when the Sun its at its _____ point in the sky.	Without a source of _____, there are no shadows at all.	As the Sun appears to move across the sky, the shadow made by a stick changes in length and _____.
Outside, shadows are made when light from the _____ is blocked.	When the Sun is at its highest point in the sky, the shadows are _____.	When the Sun is lowest in the sky, the shadows are _____.

The Sun and the Earth

During the **day** we see the **Sun**. It appears to **rise** in the **east** and move across the **sky** until it appears to set in the **west** in the **evening**. But really, the Sun does not move at all!

It is dangerous to look at the Sun directly, as the **light** can damage our eyes. We know that the Sun is a **sphere**. Our **Earth** is also **spherical**. Each day the Earth rotates. This means it turns on its **axis**, an imaginary line through its centre. It makes a complete turn once every 24 hours.

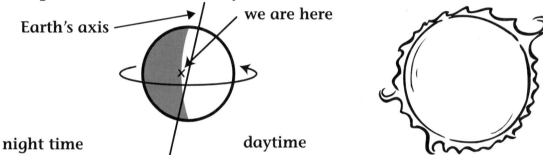

We can see the Sun during the **daytime**, because our side of the Earth is facing the Sun. At night, when the Earth has rotated (turned) around, it is dark because our side of the Earth is facing away from the Sun. When we see the **sunrise**, it is because we are just coming into the **sunlight**.

When we see the **sunset**, the Earth has rotated and we are just going into **darkness**. The Sun appears to pass below the **horizon**.

Another spherical object in **space** is the **Moon**. The Moon goes around the Earth roughly once in a **month**. As with the Earth, half of the Moon is **lit** by the Sun. The Moon does not make any light of its own. At different times of the month, we can see a different amount of the lit side of the Moon.

The Sun and the Earth

1. Explain how day and night happen.

_____

_____

_____

2. How much of the Earth is lit by the Sun at any one time?

_____

3. During the day, the Sun appears to move across the sky. The Sun does not really move. Explain what causes sunrise and sunset.

Sunset _____

_____

Sunrise _____

_____

4. What is the horizon?

_____

_____

5. How much of the Moon is lit by the Sun?

_____

6. Can we see all of the lit side of the Moon in the nights throughout each month?

_____

_____

Draw diagrams and write explanations of how sunrise, midday, sunset and midnight happen. Describe the positions of the Sun and the Earth in each explanation.

The Sun and the Earth

1. During the day, the Sun appears to move across the sky. It is not really moving. What is happening?

_____

_____

2. What shape is the Sun? Circle the correct answer.

cube   sphere   circle

3. List two other objects in space that are the same shape.

_____

4. How much of the Earth is lit by the Sun?

_____

5. What causes the night? Underline the correct answer.

The Sun goes behind clouds.

The Sun goes round to the other side of the Earth.

The Moon gets in the way of the Sun.

The Earth turns round, so we are facing away from the Sun.

6. Which object in space travels around the Earth?

_____

7. Why does the Moon not seem to be the same shape all the time?

_____

_____

 Explain how sunrise, midday, sunset and midnight happen. Draw diagrams to help you. Describe the positions of the Sun and the Earth each time.

Find the correct explanation

Each of six pupils has written an explanation for day and night.
Find the correct one and explain why each of the others is incorrect.

When it is daytime the Sun comes up. When it is night the Sun goes down. The Earth stays still. The Sun just goes up and down.

correct/incorrect _____

The Sun travels around the Earth. When the Sun is round our side, it is daytime. When it is round the other side, it is night-time here, but they are having daytime on the other side. It takes 24 hours for the Sun to go round the Earth.

correct/incorrect _____

The Earth travels round the Sun once each day. When we are in front of the Sun it is daytime, but when we go behind the Sun we are facing away from it so it is dark.

correct/incorrect _____

In the night, the Moon moves around the Earth and goes across in front of the Sun. The Sun cannot be seen from the Earth. In the daytime, the Moon moves out of the way behind the Earth.

correct/incorrect _____

In the night the Sun is covered by thick cloud. The clouds move away or get thinner in the daytime, so the Sun can shine on the Earth.

correct/incorrect _____

In the daytime our side of the Earth is facing the Sun, so it is light. By the night-time, the Earth has rotated around and our side is dark. The other side is having daytime.

correct/incorrect _____

Enlarge to A3 size.

Sun and Earth quiz

The questions for this quiz have been lost. Make a question card to go with each answer card. Then cut out the cards and mix them up. Ask your friend to match up the pairs.

Q	A	Q	A
	They are spherical.		The Earth rotates on its axis.
	Our side of the Earth is facing away from the Sun.		Our side of the Earth is facing towards the Sun.
	Where we are on the Earth is just coming into sunlight.		The Sun appears to move across the sky, but really the Earth is moving.
	This is when the Sun is just disappearing over the horizon.		It goes around the Earth about once in a month.
	We see different amounts of the lit side at different times of the month.		It reflects the light of the Sun.

Sun and Earth demonstration

These pupils are demonstrating how day and night happen and how the Moon appears to change shape. Explain what they are doing, using the words in the box.

One pupil is holding _____

_____

_____

The torch is the _____

_____

_____

_____

_____

_____

_____

day	night	sunrise	sunset	Earth
Moon	Sun shine	light	dark	
rotate	revolve	half	lit	month
sunlight	daylight	darkness	hours	

Space diagrams

Cut out the pictures and labels. Stick the label 'Day and night' onto a piece of paper as a title. Use some of the pictures and labels to make a labelled diagram that shows how day and night happen.

Use the leftover pictures and labels to make another diagram that shows how a year happens.

The Earth travels around the Sun.

A year

This takes 24 hours.

Day and night

Light from the Sun

The Earth rotates.

This takes 365 days.

Light

Dark

Sun and Earth crossword

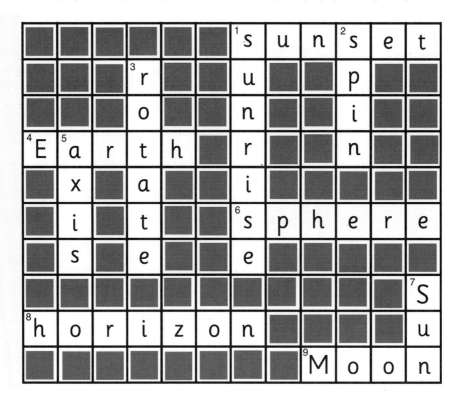

Write clues for the words in this crossword.

Across

1. The time when the Sun appears to go down. (6)

4. _____ (5)

6. _____ (6)

8. _____ (7)

9. _____ (4)

Down

1. The time when _____ (7)

2. _____ (4)

3. _____ (6)

5. _____ (4)

7. _____ (3)

Energy and electricity

Electricity can be made from **renewable energy sources** such as **wind** and **water**. These energy sources are called 'renewable' because they will never run out.

Electricity can also be made from **non-renewable energy sources** such as **coal**, **oil** and **gas**. These energy sources will run out one day.

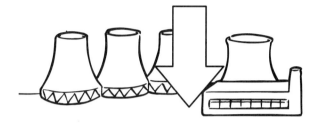

Wind power is used to turn wind **turbines** that make machines called **generators** turn. The **movement energy** from the wind is changed into **electrical energy**. When **water power** is used to make electricity, the water turns huge turbines inside a **dam**. The turbines are like waterwheels. They make generators turn, changing movement energy into electrical energy.

In this type of **power station** the **fuel** (coal, oil or gas) is burned in a **furnace**. The heat is used to boil water, producing steam that is used to turn **turbines**. The turbines make machines called **generators** turn, changing **movement energy** into **electrical energy**. **Rubbish** could be burned instead of coal, oil or gas to do the same thing.

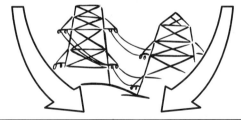

Electrical energy is brought to our homes, schools, shops and factories by **cables** that are held high up on **pylons** or buried underground. The electrical energy is then turned into more useful forms of energy to give us **heat**, **light** and **sound**, and to make things **move**.

Energy and electricity

1. Explain the terms **renewable** and **non-renewable**.

_____

_____

2. Explain how one energy source can be used to make electricity.

_____

_____

3. How is making electricity from water power similar to making electricity by burning oil?

_____

_____

4. Explain how electricity gets to your home.

_____

_____

5. List some things in your home that convert electrical energy to heat, light, sound and movement energy.

electric → heat	electric → light	electric → sound	electric → movement

List one advantage and one disadvantage of using each of these energy sources to make electricity: wind, water, coal, oil, rubbish. You could draw a table.

Energy and electricity

1. Draw lines to match these two words with their meanings.

renewable   will run out

non-renewable   will never run out

2. Draw lines to match the energy sources with the correct words.

coal

oil   renewable

wind

gas   non-renewable

water

3. All of these energy sources can be changed into _____
energy. (Fill the gap.)

4. Explain how water held back by a dam can be used to make electricity.

_____

5. Explain how electricity gets to your home.

_____

6. List some things in your home that change electrical energy to heat, light, sound and movement energy.

electric → heat	electric → light	electric → sound	electric → movement

List an advantage and a disadvantage of using each of these energy sources to make electricity: wind, water, coal, oil. You could draw a table like this:

Energy source	Advantage	Disadvantage
wind		

Energy and electricity concept map

On the diagram below, find two words that are linked and draw a line between them. Write on the line why you have joined those words. One example has already been done for you.

Now join together as many pairs of words as you can. Each time, write on the line why you have joined them. You can use each word more than once.

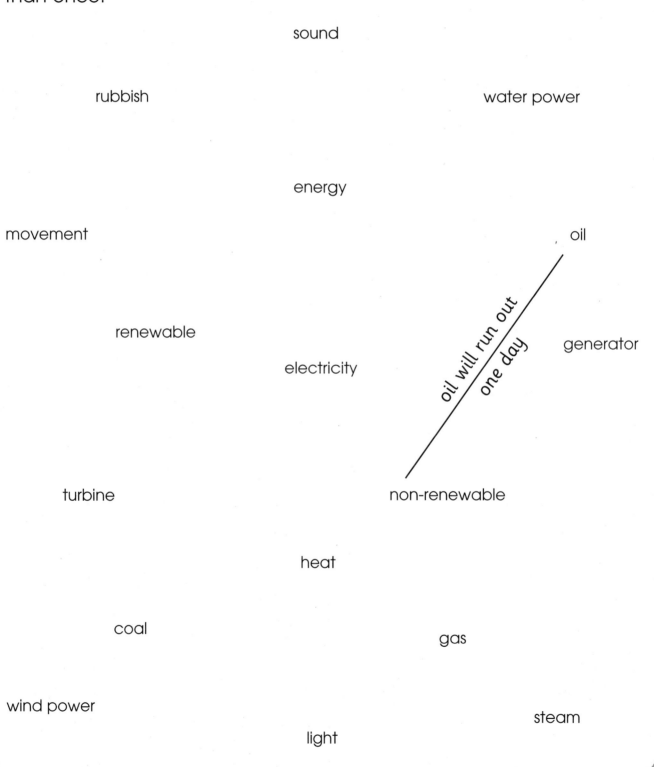

sound

rubbish

water power

energy

movement

oil

renewable

electricity

generator

oil will run out

one day

turbine

non-renewable

heat

coal

gas

wind power

steam

light